GIOACCHINO ROSSINI

IL BARBIERE DI SIVIGLIA
THE BARBER OF SEVILLE
DER BARBIER VON SEVILLA

Overture to the Opera

T0080320

Ernst Eulenburg Ltd

London · Mainz · Madrid · New York · Paris · Prague · Tokyo · Toronto · Zürich

CONTENTS

PREFACE

Towards the end of the 19th century, Verdi expressed the view that *Il Barbiere di Siviglia* was the most beautiful *opera buffa* ever written. However its first performance on 20 February 1816 was somewhat chaotic. This seems to have been due partly to deliberate attempts to undermine Rossini by supporters of Paisiello, who had written a well-known *Barbiere* some time before; at the premiere itself there was jeering, the farcical chasing of an errant cat that had somehow invaded the stage, as well as derisive criticism from the auditorium of the composer's new gold and yellow jacket, worn especially for the event. Rossini had in fact acknowledged the elder composer's work – even giving his new opera a different title, *Almaviva, ossia L'inutil precauzione (Almaviva or The Futile Precaution)*, and had indeed written to Paisiello to express his respect for him. He had also pointed out the changes that had been made to the text in deference to Paisiello: a futile precaution indeed, it seems. The opera's popularity has, notwithstanding, remained undimmed since its first season, the second performance contrastingly having been hailed a triumph. *Il Barbiere* was Rossini's 17th stage work and broadly speaking marks the mid-point of his operatic output.

To a degree the present overture has a misleading association with the opera to which it is now linked. This music had been heard twice before: as an overture firstly to the now-obscure *Aureliano in Palmira*, premiered in December 1813, and secondly in the opera *Elisabetta, Regina d'Inghilterra* written the same year (1815) he received his contract for *Barbiere*. It is interesting that the music of this overture has links with material in the opera *Aureliano* itself, making its reuse perhaps a curious decision on Rossini's part. But considered simply as a freestanding curtain-raiser it is, in common with many of Rossini's overtures, endlessly arresting and effective.

The overture demonstrates structurally typical features of Rossini's overtures by the time he wrote the present example. A slow *maestoso* introduction, here with distinctive *balbettando* demisemiquavers for strings and bassoons, as well as a more lyrical idea for violins and flute is followed by an embryonic sonata-form 'exposition'. Two themes are presented in the *Allegro vivace*: a stealthily comical E minor theme with a martial fortissimo outburst at b48 and the G major melody at b92 with the halting, dotted-rhythms of a chromatically rising major second. This 'exposition' is concluded with one of Rossini's famous, long range *crescendi* – a build-up of tension across 36 bars in which tonic and dominant relentlessly alternate as *pianissimo* strings and *dolce* winds rise to a triumphant *fortissimo*, at which point the drama subsides into an immediate recapitulation. This idiosyncratic stamp of Rossini's musical identity first arose in his opera *L'inganno felice* premiered in 1812 and has become synonymous with the composer; it led Rossini's detractors – those in fact who supported Paisiello – to disparagingly nickname him 'Signor Crescendo'. After the recapitulation has taken its course, the *crescendo* idea is truncated at b225, losing its last 12 bars to a suddenly faster coda; it hastens the end with a precipitous descending chromatic line in the first and second violins at bb229–233 and bb242–246, pushing hard against the insistent cadence of the last 20 bars.

David Lewiston Sharpe

VORWORT

Ende des 19. Jahrhunderts brachte Verdi die Meinung zum Ausdruck, dass *Il Barbiere di Siviglia* die schönste Opera buffa sei, die je geschrieben wurde. Die Uraufführung am 20. Februar 1816 verlief jedoch ein wenig chaotisch. Dies scheint teilweise auf absichtliche Versuche der Anhänger Paisiellos zurückzugehen, die Rossinis Arbeit unterminieren wollten. Paisiello hatte nämlich einige Zeit zuvor eine allgemein bekannte Vertonung des *Barbiere di Siviglia* komponiert. Während der Uraufführung von Rossinis Oper johlte das Publikum, eine Katze, die irgendwie auf die Bühne gelangt war, wurde gejagt und Rossinis neue goldgelbe Jacke, die er extra zu diesem Anlass trug, wurde vom Publikum höhnisch kritisiert. Rossini hatte das Werk des älteren Komponisten jedoch respektiert und gab seiner neuen Oper sogar einen anderen Titel: *Almaviva, ossia L'inutil precauzione* („Almaviva oder Die vergebliche Vorsichtsmaßnahme"). Auch hatte er Paisiello geschrieben, um ihm Respekt zu zollen und auf die Textänderungen hinzuweisen, die er aus diesem Grund vorgenommen hatte – in der Tat eine „vergebliche Vorsichtsmaßnahme", wie es scheint. Ungeachtet dessen blieb der Erfolg von Rossinis Oper seit jener Saison ungetrübt, denn die zweite Aufführung war im Gegensatz zur ersten ein großer Erfolg. *Il Barbiere di Siviglia* war Rossinis 17. Bühnenwerk und markiert den Mittelpunkt seines Opernschaffens.

In gewissem Maße steht die vorliegende Ouvertüre in einem irreführenden Zusammenhang mit der Oper, mit der sie jetzt verbunden ist. Die Musik wurde zuvor schon zweimal verwendet: zuerst als Ouvertüre zu dem verschollenen Werk *Aureliano in Palmira*, uraufgeführt im Dezember 1813, und dann zu der Oper *Elisabetta, Regina d'Inghilterra* aus dem Jahr 1815, die im selben Jahr komponiert wurde, in dem Rossini seinen Vertrag für *Il Barbiere di Siviglia* erhielt. Interessant ist, dass die Musik dieser Ouvertüre Material aus der Oper *Aureliano* enthält. Somit erscheint die Wiederverwendung der Ouvertüre etwas merkwürdig. Betrachtet man sie jedoch einfach nur als allein stehendes kurzes Vorspiel, so ist sie, genauso wie viele andere Ouvertüren Rossinis, unglaublich faszinierend und wirkungsvoll.

Die Ouvertüre weist strukturell typische Merkmale von Rossinis Ouvertüren aus dieser Zeit auf. Der langsamen Einleitung (maestoso) mit den charakteristischen Zweiunddreißigstelnoten (balbettando) in den Streichern und Fagotten und dem eher lyrischen Motiv in den Violinen und Flöten folgt der Keim einer Sonatenform-Exposition. Im Allegro vivace werden zwei Themen vorgestellt: ein verstohlen-komisches Thema in e-Moll mit einem martialischen Fortissimo-Ausbruch in Takt 48 und die G-Dur-Melodie in Takt 92 mit dem zögernden punktierten Rhythmus in chromatisch aufsteigenden großen Sekunden. Diese „Exposition" endet mit einem von Rossinis berühmten lang andauernden Crescendi. Die Spannungskurve, in der Tonika und Dominante unaufhörlich in den Streichern (pianissimo) und Bläsern (dolce) alternieren, steigt über 36 Takte hinweg bis zum triumphierenden Fortissimo. An diesem Punkt lässt die Dramatik etwas nach und es geht unmittelbar in die Reprise über. Dieser für Rossini so typische Aufbau erschien zum ersten Mal in seiner Oper *L'inganno felice*, die 1812 uraufgeführt wurde, und wurde schließlich mit dem Komponisten gleichgesetzt. Dies brachte Rossinis Kritiker – die Anhänger Paisiellos – dazu, ihn geringschätzig als „Signor Crescendo" zu bezeichnen. Nachdem die Reprise durchlaufen ist, wird das Crescendo in Takt 225 abgebrochen und verliert die letzten zwölf Takte zugunsten einer plötzlich schnelleren Coda. Sie beschleunigt den Schluss mit einer sich überschlagenden chromatischen Abwärtslinie in den ersten und zweiten Violinen (T. 229–233 und T. 242–246) und setzt sich stark gegen die beharrliche Kadenz in den letzten 20 Takten durch.

David Lewiston Sharpe
Übersetzung: Uta Heipp

IL BARBIERE DI SIVIGLIA
Overture to the Opera

Gioacchino Rossini
(1792–1868)

I. **Andante maestoso**

No. 685   EE 3777

6

8

14

16

20

21

24